PIXEL COLORING ADVENTURE

SECTION 1:

DINOSAURS

AND OTHER PREHISTORIC

CREATURES

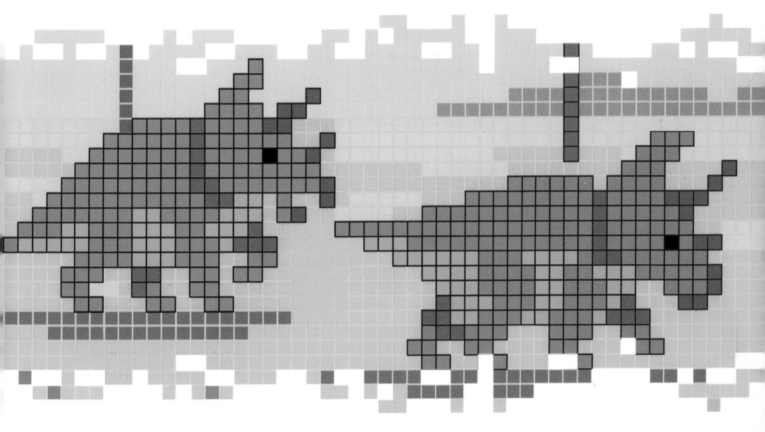

An Imprint of Sterling Publishing
1166 Avenue of the Americas
New York, NY 10036

SANDY CREEK and the distinctive Sandy Creek logo are registered trademarks of Barnes & Noble, Inc.
Text © 2015 Tide Mill Media. Illustrations © 2015 Tide Mill Media.
This 2015 edition published by Sandy Creek.

ISBN 978-1-4351-6273-0
Manufactured in Zhejiang, China
Lot #:
0 2 4 6 8 10 9 7 5 3 1
11/15

Triceratops

This plant-eating dinosaur's name means "three horned face."
It had an impressive bony frill around its neck too!

Ankylosaurus

Ankylosaurus was covered in protective spikes and plates of bone.
Predators had to watch out for its powerful clubbed tail!

Herd Behavior

Triceratops lived in herds, just like cattle do today. Young Triceratops were kept in the middle of the herd to protect them from predators.

Brachiosaurus

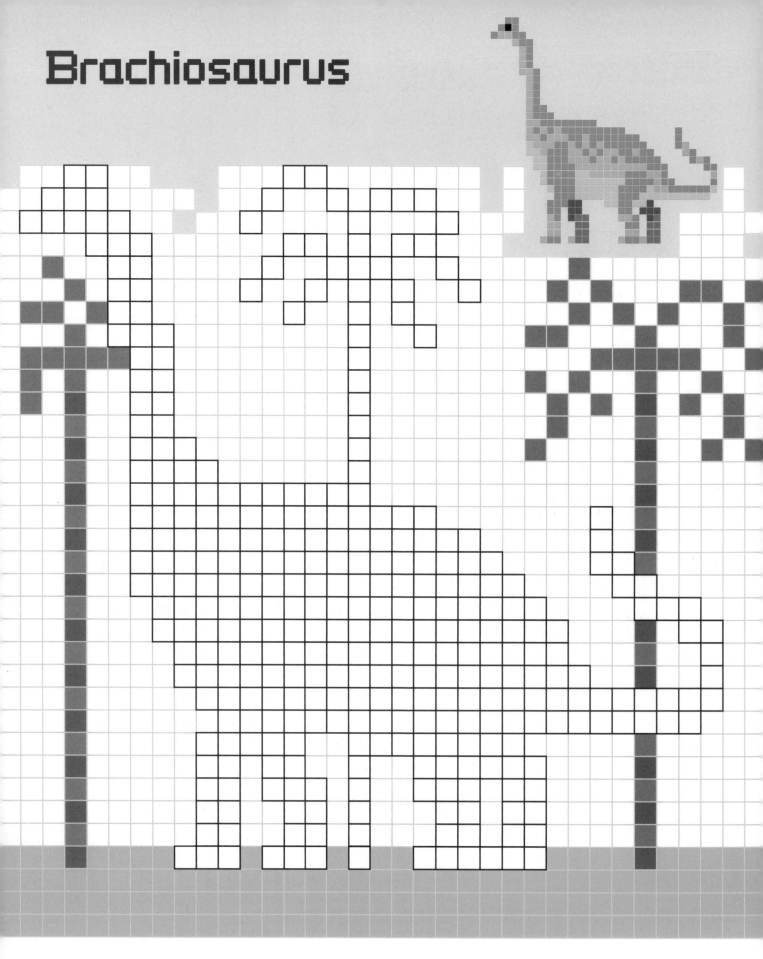

The enormous, plant-eating Brachiosaurus reached 82 feet in length!
It had a long tail and neck, and nostrils on the top of its head.

Giganotosaurus

This fearsome predator weighed more than a T. rex and had enormous jaws, packed with razor-sharp teeth!

Feeding Time

With their incredibly long necks, this herd of Brachiosaurus are munching on leaves from the tops of the trees.

Parasaurolophus

This dinosaur had a long hollow crest at the back of its head. The crest may have been used to make loud noises to other members of the herd.

Protoceratops

This plant eater had a parrot-like beak and a large bony head frill. It was only about 6 feet long—snack size for a hungry theropod!

Spinosaurus

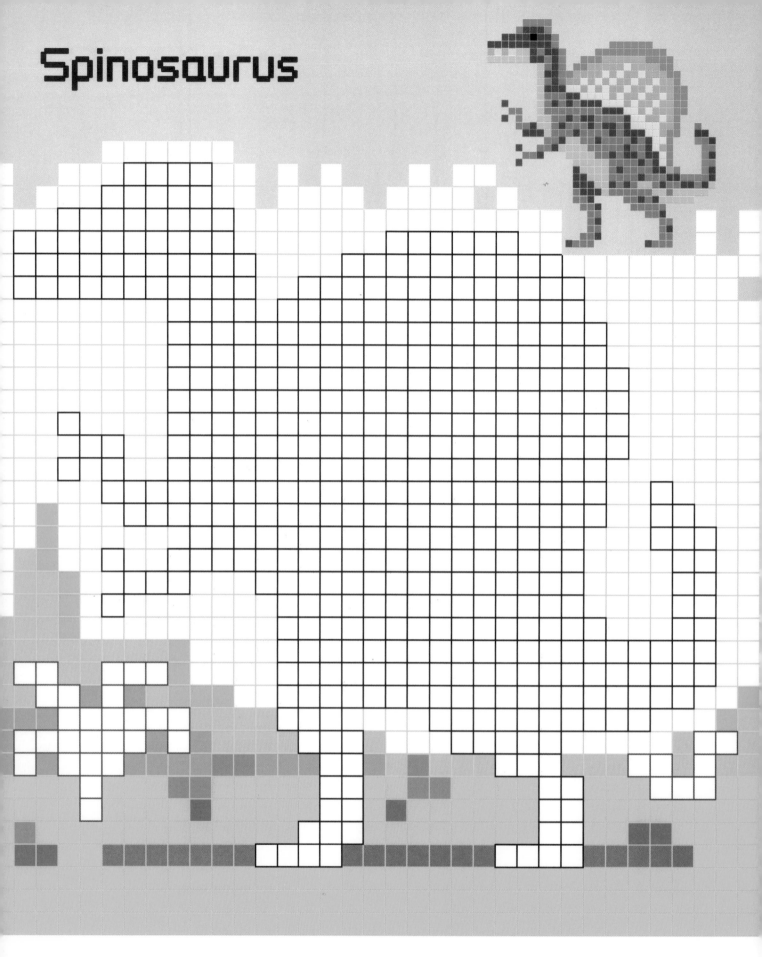

With a distinctive sail on its back, Spinosaurus is one of the largest known carnivorous (meat-eating) dinosaurs.

Stegosaurus

Easily recognizable by the plates on its back and its spiked tail, this giant armored dinosaur had a tiny brain for its size.

Looking for Food

Stegosaurus were about the same size as a modern bus!

They needed to eat a lot of plants, such as mosses, ferns, horsetails, and conifers in order to survive.

Tyrannosaurus rex

The "king of the tyrant reptiles" had teeth like steak knives and a bite that was three times more powerful than a modern lion's!

Hadrosaur

This duck-billed dinosaur had loads of teeth and a hinged jaw that helped it to grind up huge quantities of vegetation.

T. rex Attack!

These hadrosaurs are looking for some nice plants to eat. Little do they suspect that it could be their last meal!

Graciliceratops

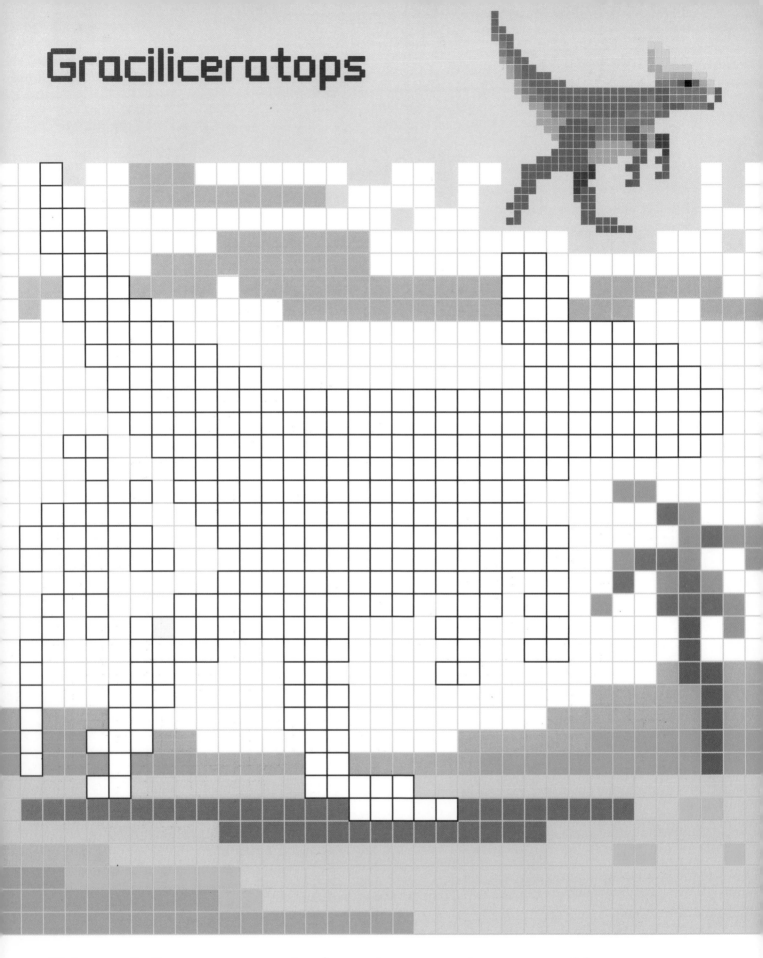

This small dinosaur was only about the same size as a cat! Its name means "graceful horned face."

Diplodocus

At 90 feet in length, this giant herbivore had a long neck and a whip-like tail. Diplodocus swallowed stones to help grind up plants in its stomach.

Pachycephalosaurus

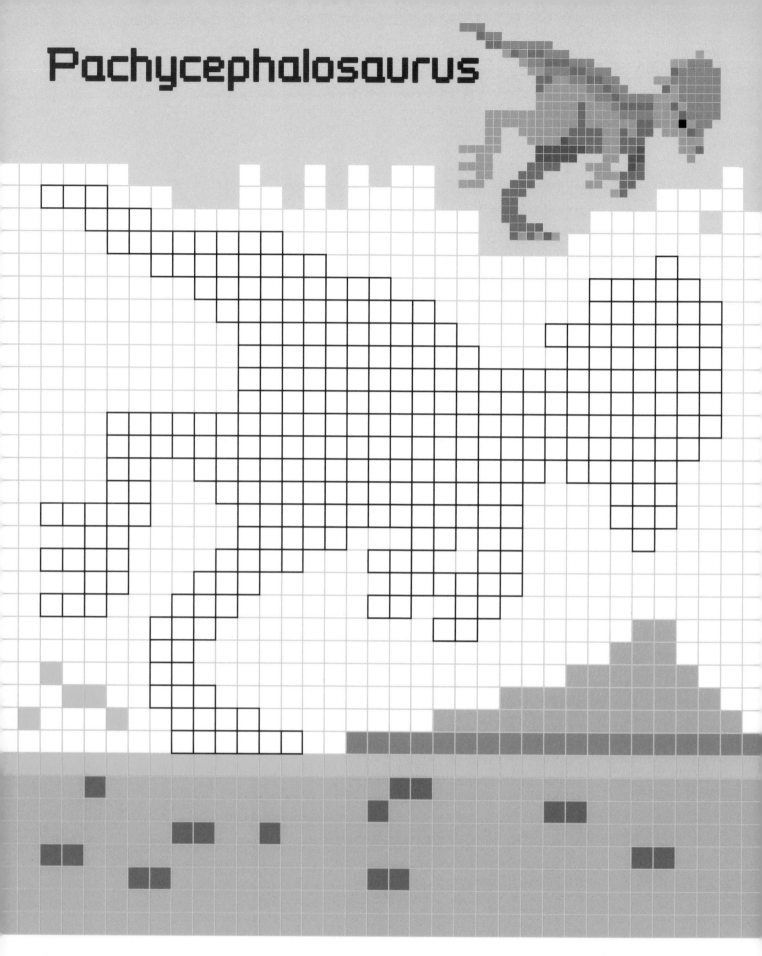

Pachycephalosaurus butted heads when competing with rivals. It's just as well they had a thick bony skull to protect their brain!

Archaeopteryx

This small, feathered dinosaur had sharp teeth and a killing claw. Scientists think it may be the link between dinosaurs and modern birds.

Jurassic Skies

Archaeopteryx probably weren't the best fliers, but they could take flight and glide to escape from trouble and to look for prey.

Scutellosaurus

Scutellosaurus means "little-shielded lizard." It is one of the earliest known armored dinosaurs.

Deinonychus

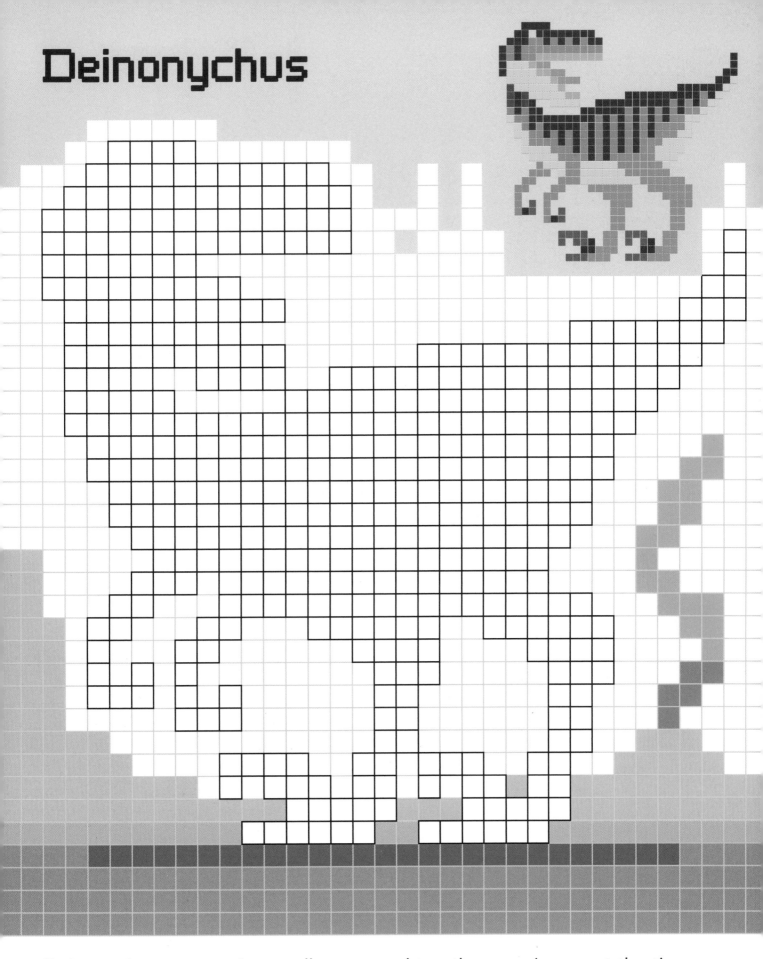

Deinonychus were quite small compared to other carnivores at the time, but they were ferocious hunters!

Pack Hunters

Deinonychus had a retractable killing claw on each foot and hunted in packs for much larger prey. Their name means "terrible claw!"

Kronosaurus

Kronosaurus was a marine reptile that lived at the time of the dinosaurs.
It fed on turtles and plesiosaurs and was a very formidable predator!

Mosasaurus

Mosasaurus belonged to the "sea lizard" family and used its powerful tail, paddle-like limbs, and sharp teeth to hunt fish close to the water's surface.

Marine Predator

The thick-bodied aquatic Mosasaurus could devour an entire school of fish in a single mouthful, and could reach 59 feet in length!

Shonisaurus

At 52 feet long and weighing 33 tons, the Shonisaurus was one of the largest animals to ever inhabit Earth.

Quetzalcoatlus

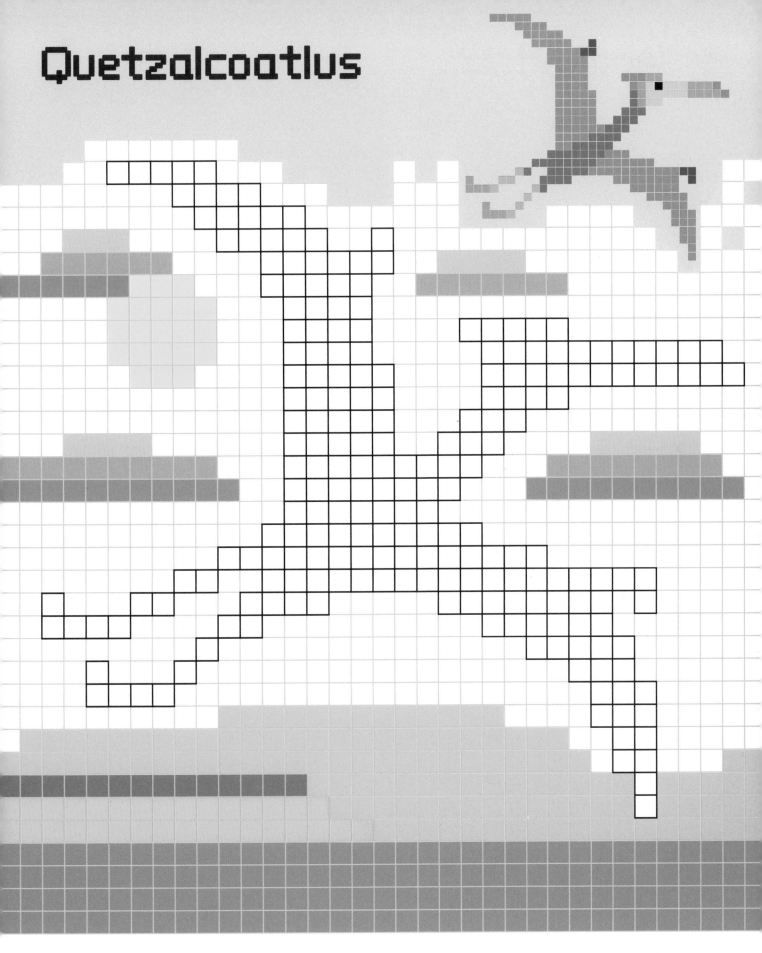

This long-necked pterosaur is one of the largest flying animals of all-time.
It had a mighty wingspan of 36 feet!

Pteranodon

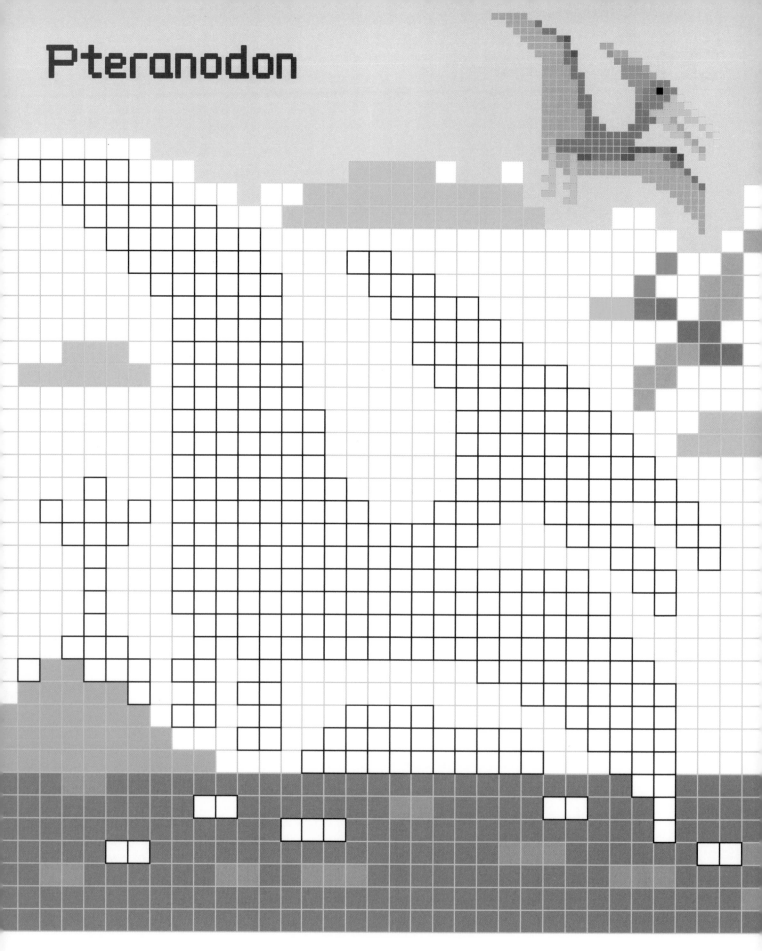

The Pteranodon was a master at catching fish in its beak and then eating them whole! It had no teeth and its name means "toothless flier."

Dimetrodon

Dimetrodon walked the Earth 40 million years before the first dinosaurs and is actually more closely related to mammals than dinosaurs!

Saber-toothed Cat

With their saber-like canine teeth, these ferocious carnivores preyed on large mammals like elephants and rhinos up until 11,000 years ago.

Giant Bear

The Giant Short-faced Bear was one of the scariest predators of the Pleistocene. Adults could rear up to 13 feet high and run 35 mph!

Megalodon

The Megalodon was one of the most powerful predators ever! With massive teeth, immense size and powerful jaws, even whales were its prey.

Dunkleosteus

Long before dinosaurs evolved, this heavily-armored 32-feet long fish
swam the oceans looking for prey.

Monster Shark!

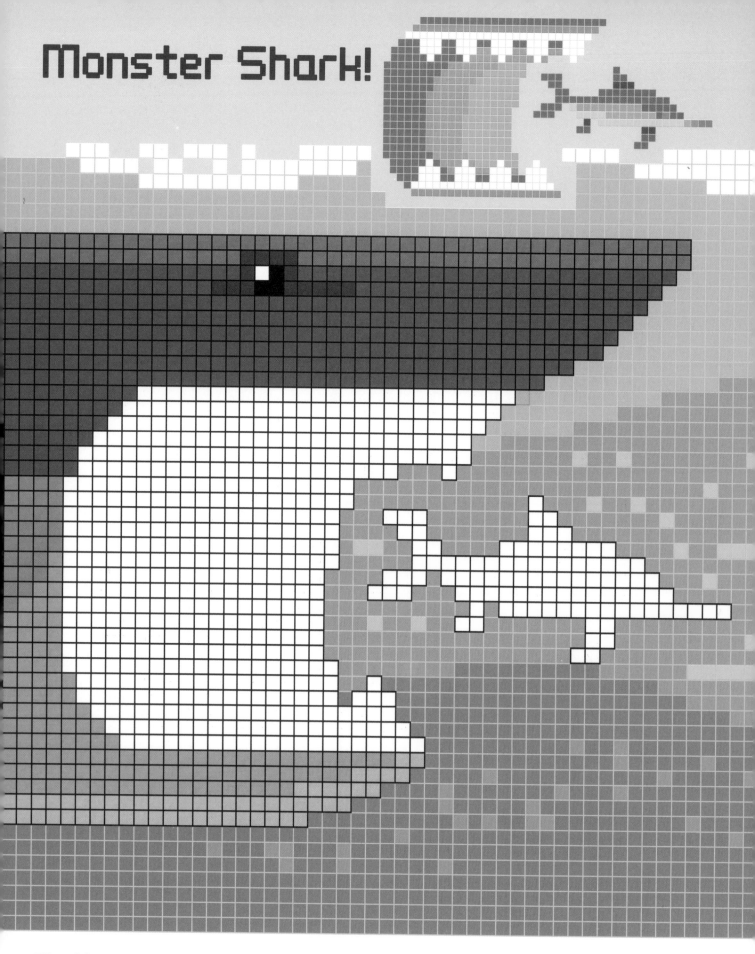

The Megalodon was the top predator in the oceans before it became extinct. Entire species migrated away from the areas it inhabited!

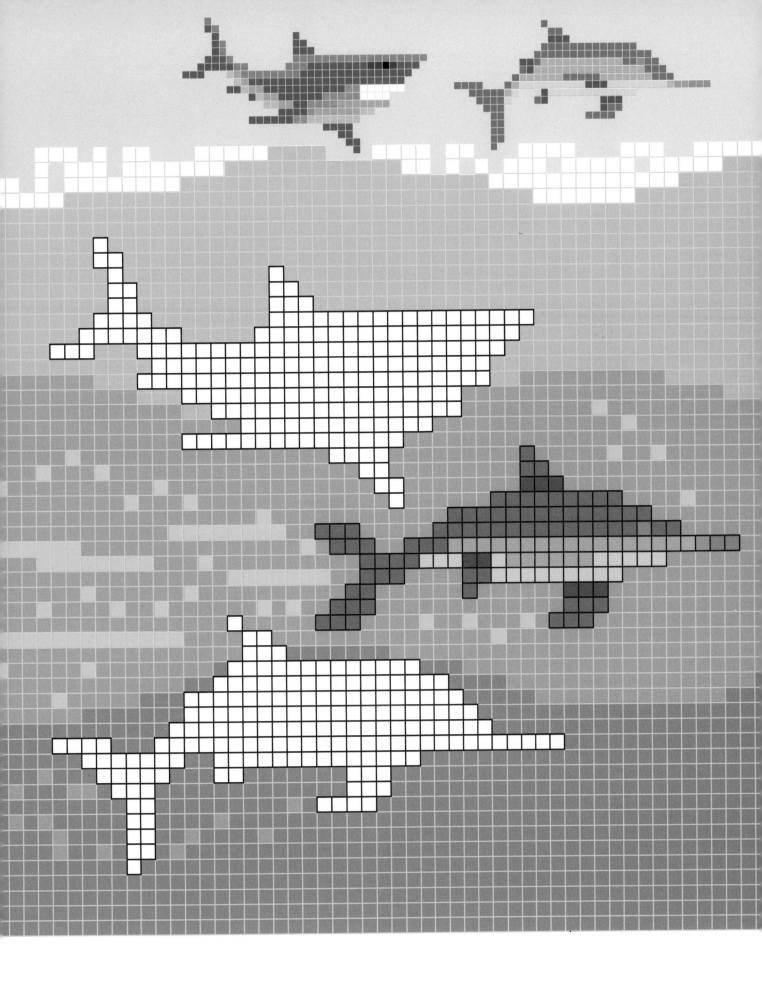

Ammonites

Ammonites are an extinct group of marine animals. Fossils of this creature's distinctive spiral-shaped shell can be found all over the world.

Dire Wolf

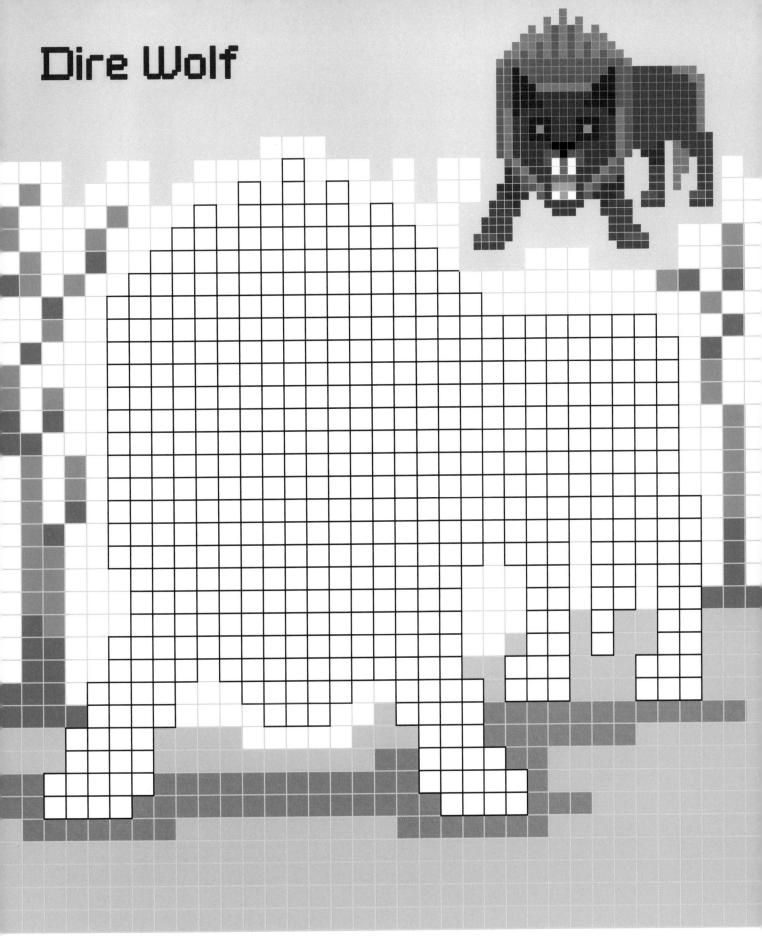

The extinct dire wolf was considerably larger than modern-day gray wolves and had bigger teeth! Like modern wolves and dogs, they hunted in packs.

Woolly Mammoth

The woolly mammoth was roughly the size of a modern African elephant, but with bigger tusks. It had thick, shaggy hair to protect it from the cold.

Woolly Rhino

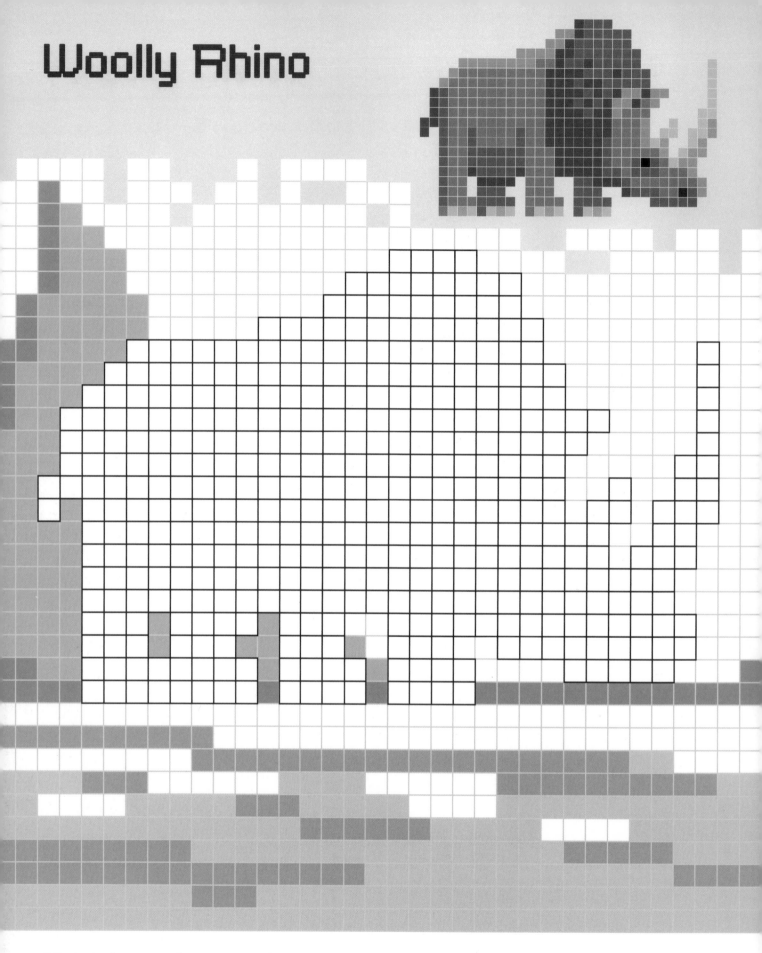

Slightly larger than a modern-day white rhino, this extinct species had thick, long fur to keep it warm in the cold, icy territories it inhabited.

PIXEL COLORING ADVENTURE

SECTION 2:

SPACE ADVENTURE

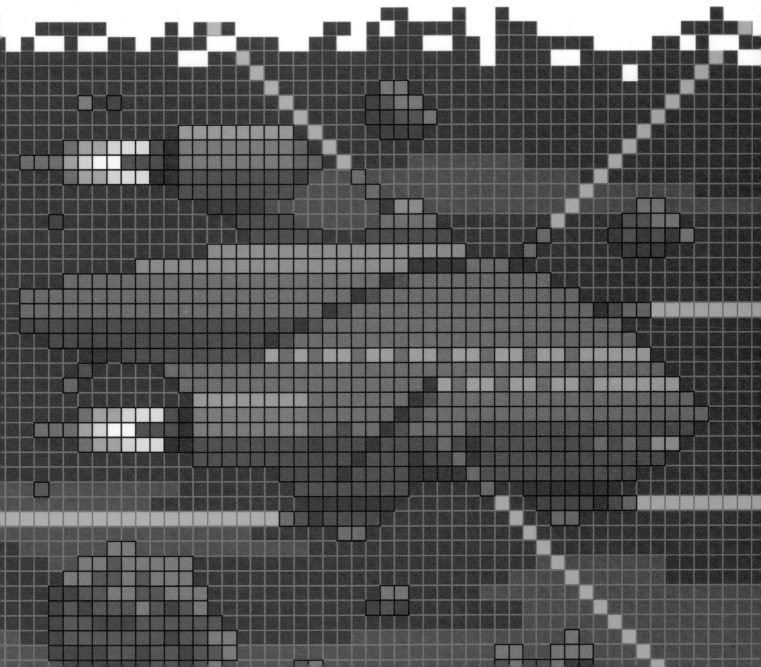

Spaceship "Quantum"

This spaceship is the pride of the Galactic Empire. Its mighty engines blast it through space at light speed! Whoosh!

Speeder

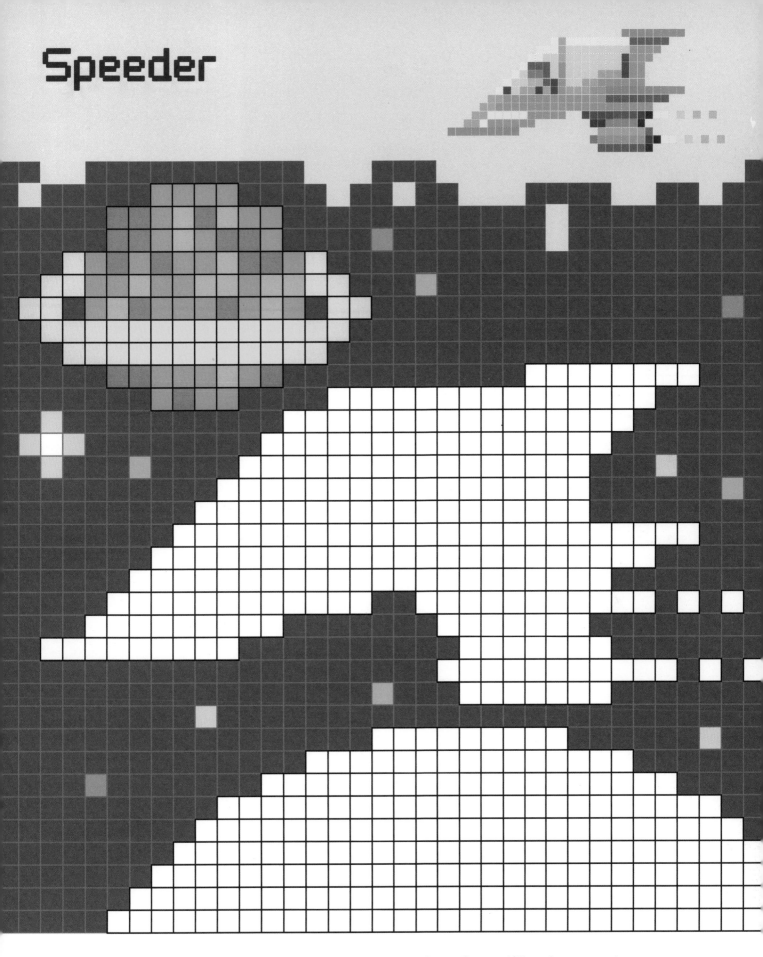

If you need to get from one planet to another fast, I'll take you in my speeder, but it will cost you! Hold on tight!

Mine Craft

These awesome mining machines travel the outer galaxy in search of precious metals and minerals. Start the drills!

Battleship

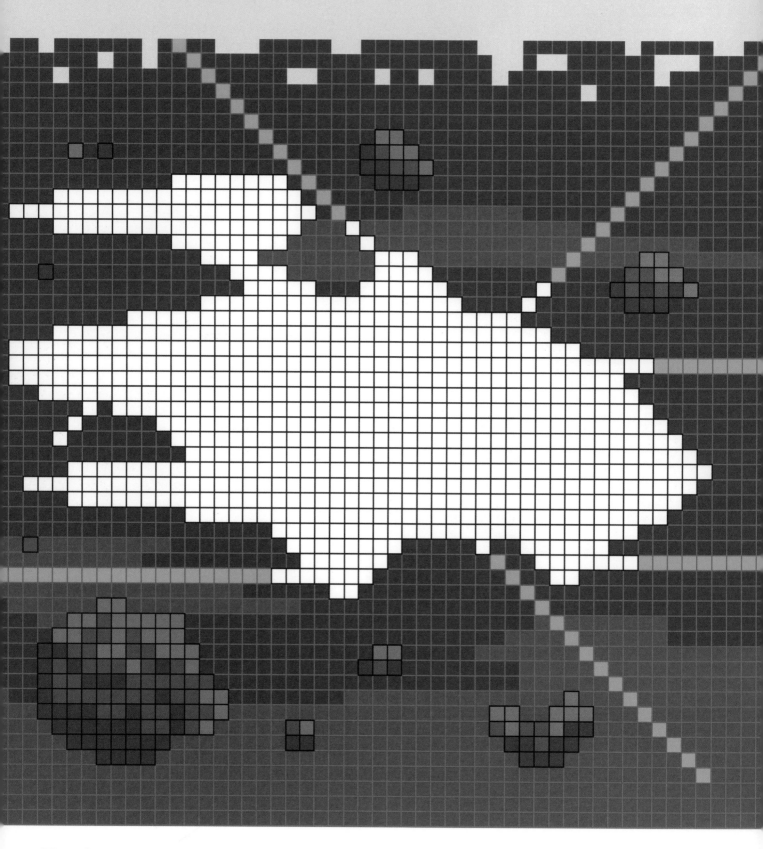

This battleship is state-of-the-art. It's testing out its new pulsar cannons on some passing asteroids. Watch out! Ka-blam!

Mega Brain

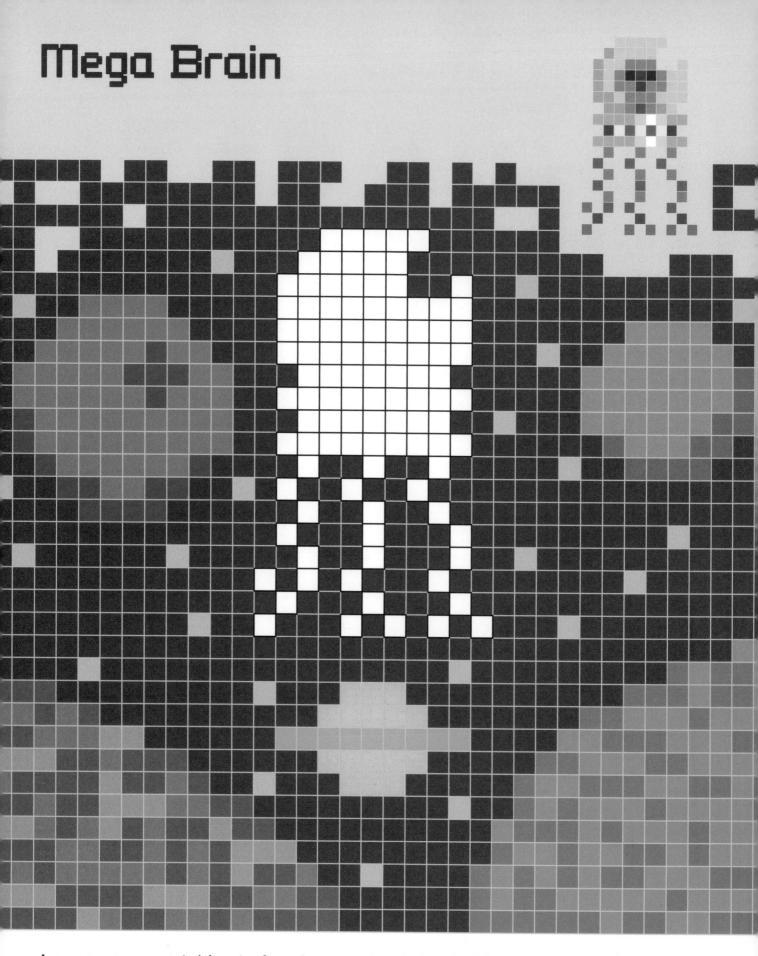

An extraterrestrial brain fitted to a robotic body, Mega Brain comes from the Plexsus Nebula in search of a new home. Bzzzzzzz!

Captain Chaos

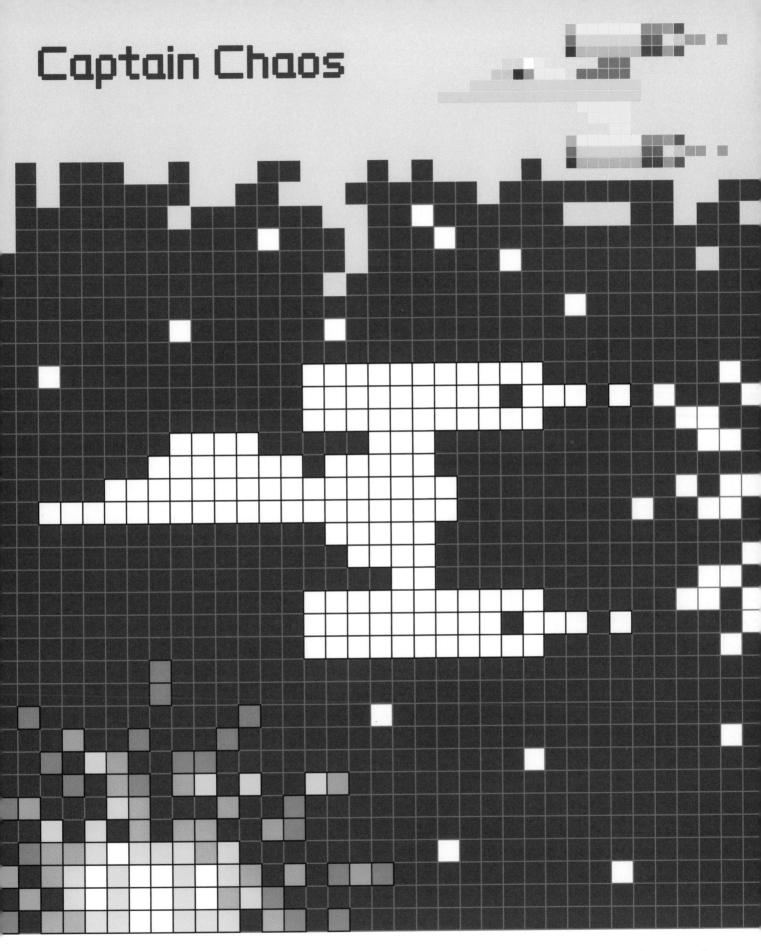

I'm a deep space flying ace in my supersonic fighter. I keep the galaxy safe from invaders by blasting them to smithereens. Take that!

Solar Sailor

Ahoy there! My craft is powered by solar rays. It's slow to accelerate but can reach enormous speeds.

Space Pirate

Space pirates roam the galaxy looking for unarmed ships to attack.
Warp the plank!

Neutreno

Neutreno is the super-intelligent leader of an alien alliance from the edge
of the Basmat system...prepare to meet your maker, earthling!

Rocket

3...2...1...Lift off! In the distant future, some people like to fly rockets from the ancient past. This 21st century rocket is so old-fashioned!

Battle Droids

Destroy! Destroy! Battle Droids roam the galaxy destroying any threat to the Galactic Empire.

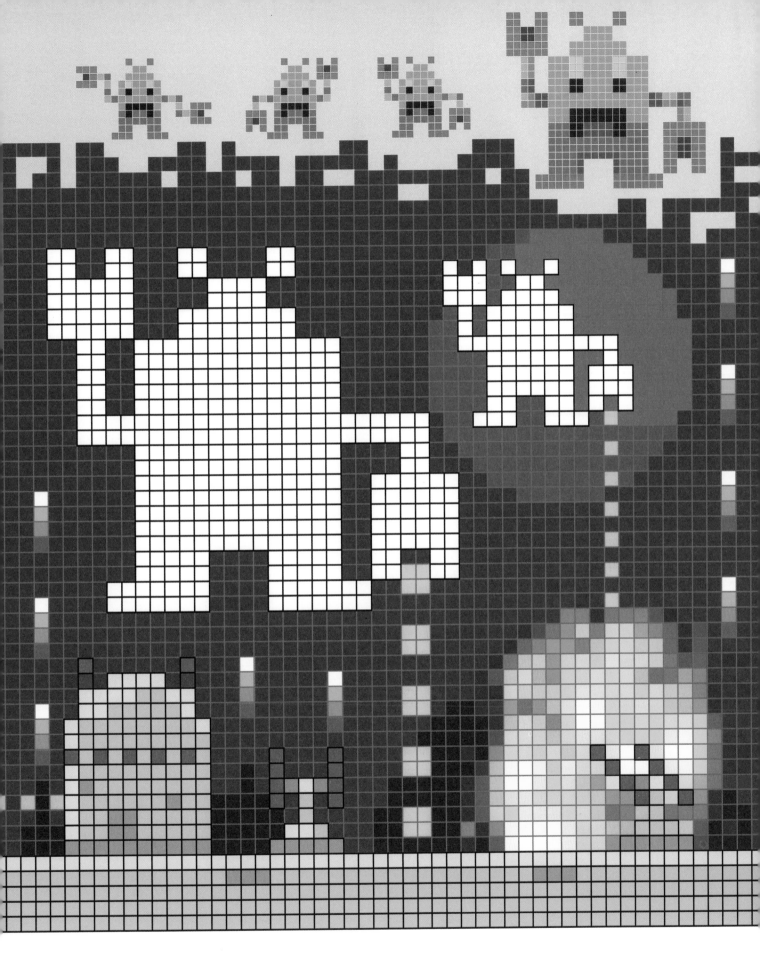

Arachnid

Dinner time! Arachnid is a massive eight-legged alien that lives in outer space. He catches his prey in enormous space webs.

Bounty Hunter

Surrender, scum! Bounty Hunter will work for anyone that pays! His laser gun and rocket boots make him a deadly enemy.

The Blip

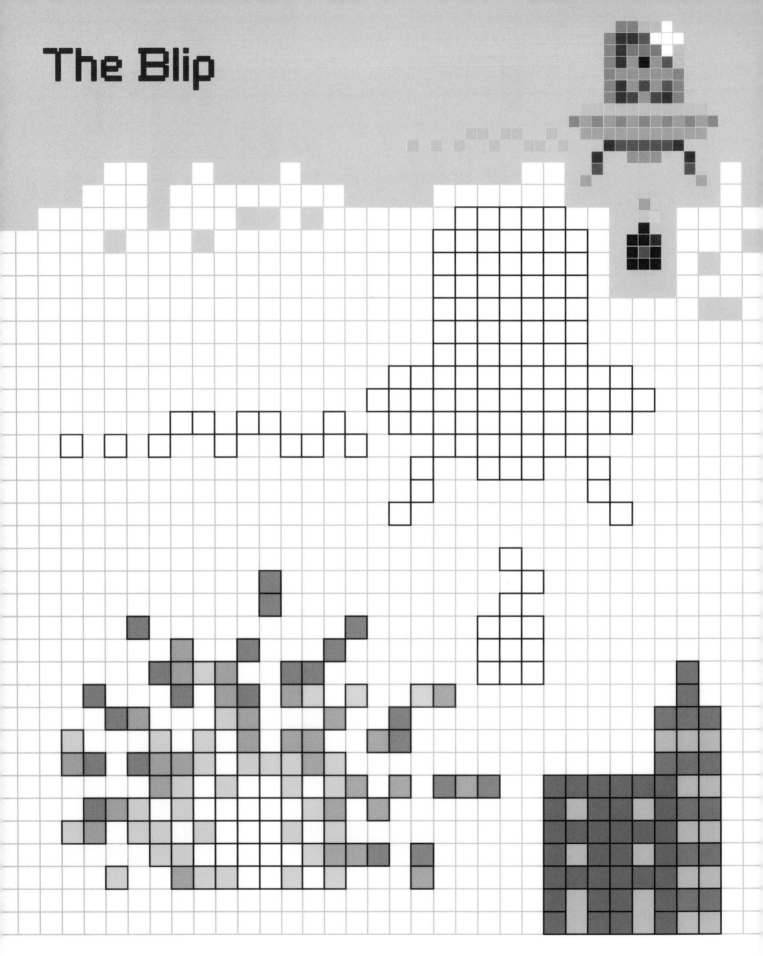

Blip...blip...BOOM! I'm just a blip on your screen—an unidentified flying object. I whizz through space, looking for new civilizations...to destroy!

Starsuit

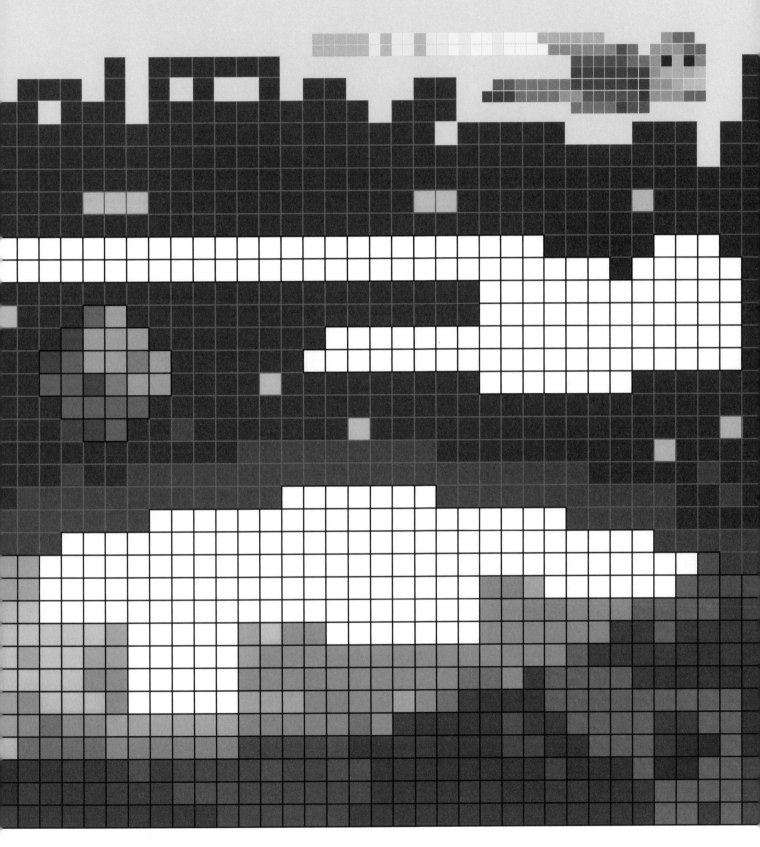

Maximum speed! A starsuit is a special spacesuit that can fly short
distances through space. It looks like this guy is in a hurry!

Rampaging Robot

Beep, beep, beep! This huge robot has gone on the rampage! It's destroying everything in its way with its red laser-beam eyes!

Apocalypse

Apocalypse's asteroid home was destroyed by a rogue mining craft. Now he's sworn to destroy the galaxy! Mwa ha ha!

Interceptor

I'm called out when an unidentified ship is spotted. My ship is fast and well-armed and I mean business! State your name and purpose!

Lord Blob

Lord Blob has declared war on the Star Council. Things could get nasty!
Bow down to your new lord!

Incoming!

The Space Station is picking up a number of unidentified flying objects.
They're not slowing down, Captain! Bleep, bleep, bleep!

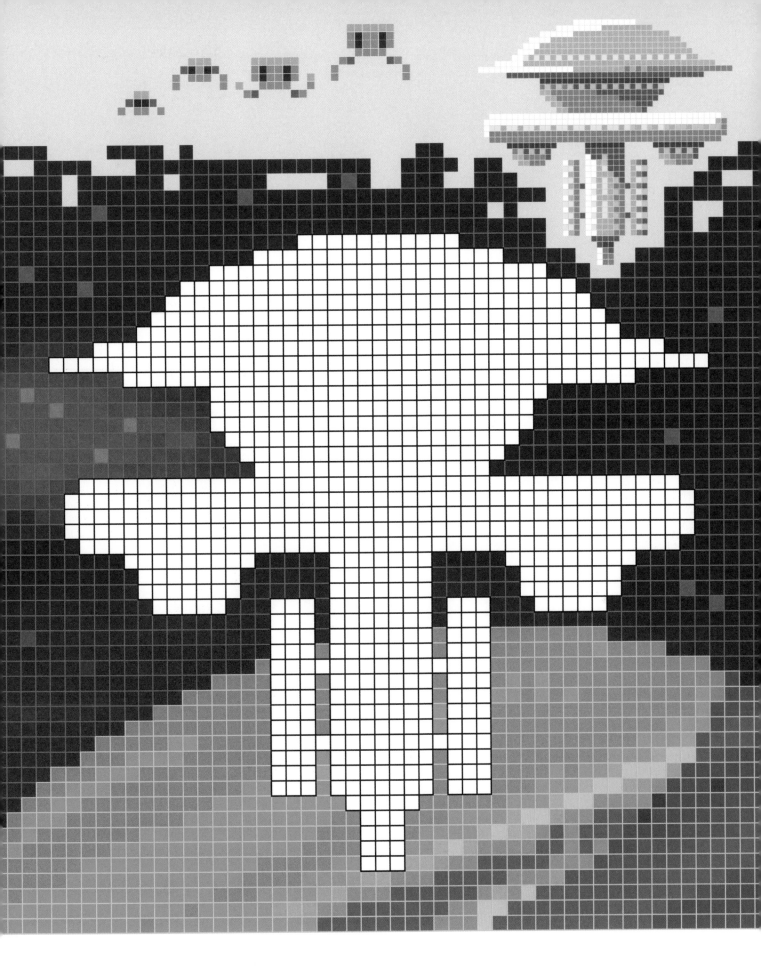

Space Station Command

This is the captain speaking...the Space Station is under attack!
All crew report to positions! Repeat, all crew report to positions!

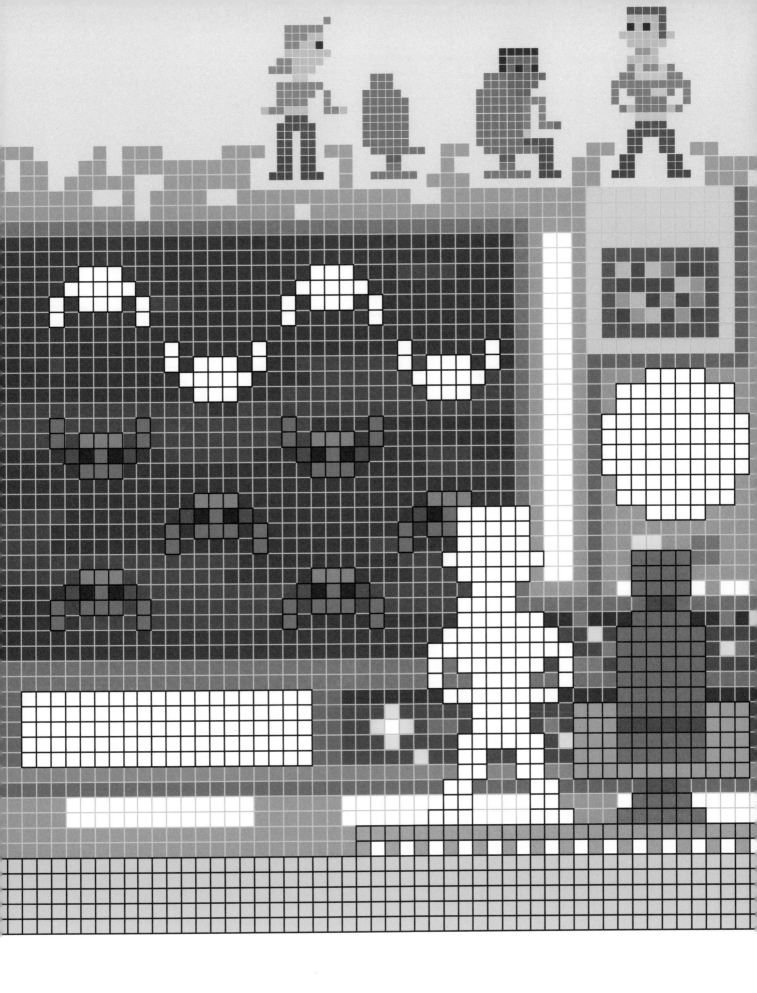

Scramble Fighters

The Space Station fighter craft have been scrambled to meet the attack, but they are heavily outnumbered.

Star Tanks

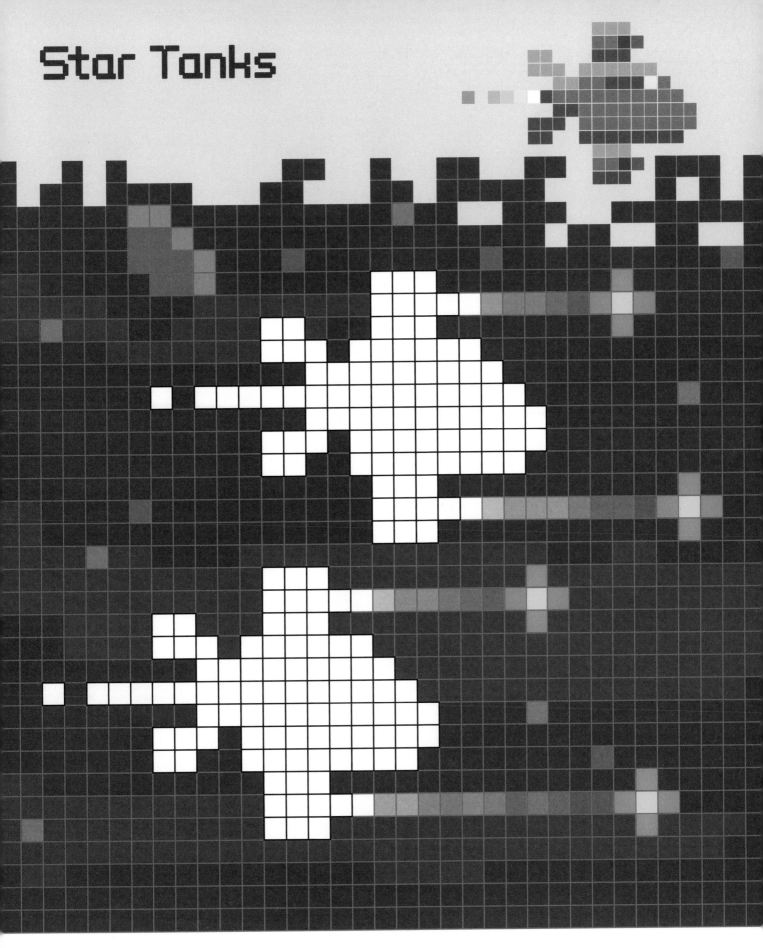

The Space Station only has a few star tanks and they are very slow, but their laser cannons pack a powerful punch. Blam! Blam! Blam!

Destroyer

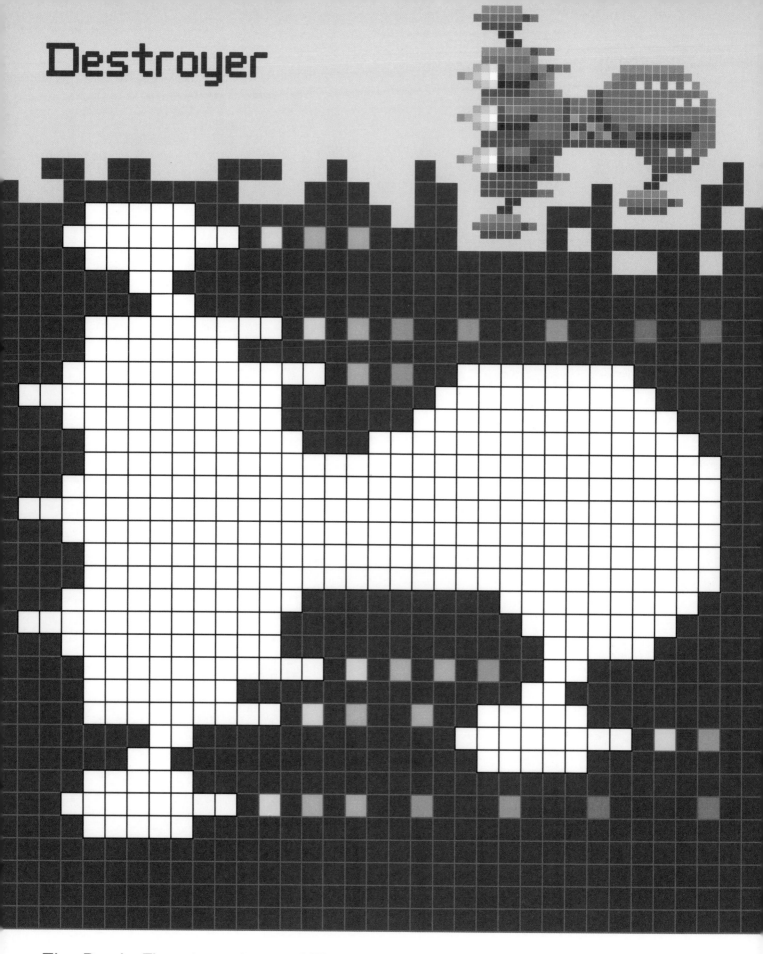

The Battle Fleet is on its way! This massive destroyer is leading the fleet into the battle. Surrender or be destroyed!

Troop Carrier

When the Battle Fleet needs to transport troopers, it uses these enormous carrier vessels. All troops report to the loading bay!

Space Battle

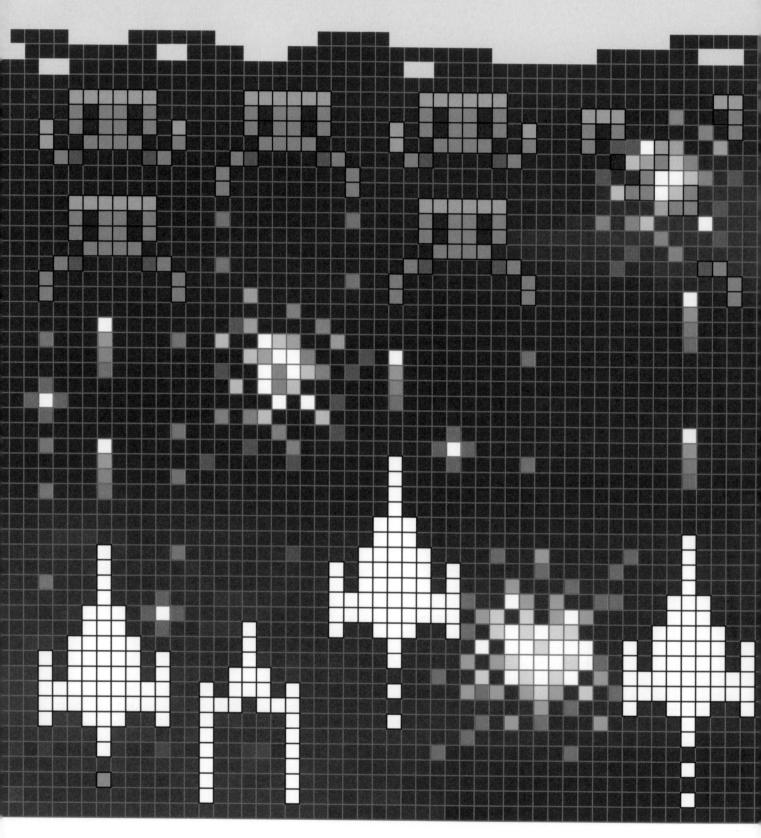

The Space Station fighters are desperately holding back the Blob attack.
Pow! Pow! Zap! Zap! Pow!

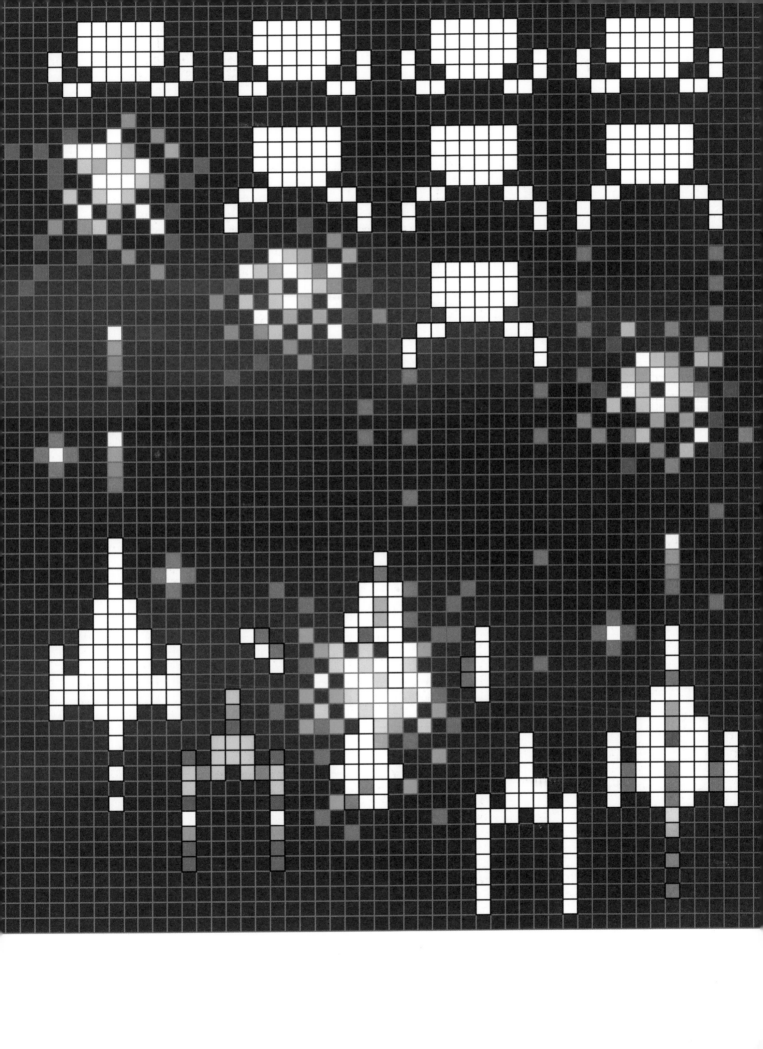

Victory

The Battle Fleet troops arrived and defeated Lord Blob's army. But nobody has spotted Lord Blob fleeing to safety. Next time, earthlings!

Mongo the Merciless

Mongo the Merciless has captured a lost fighter craft, and now he's started to eat it! Munch, munch!

Moondusa

On the dark side of a small moon lives someone you really don't want to meet! Moondusa and her terrifying space-snake hair! Sssss!

Escape Pod

Aiiiieeeeeeeee! When my ship malfunctioned I had to escape in this tiny escape pod. Now I'm re-entering the atmosphere of the planet Xantar.

Galumph

Galumph is the biggest life form ever discovered. He floats through space eating asteroids and small moons. Chomp, chomp!

Spaceship "X"

Spaceship "X" is the Battle Fleet's top-secret new craft. It's powered by thought and can travel instantly across the universe. Hold tight!

Meteor Shower

Hold on! This planet is being hit by flying space rocks! You can feel the impacts from here!

Spaceship Repair

This spaceship has hit some space junk and needs urgent repairs before it can continue. Clunk! Clunk!

Space Dragons

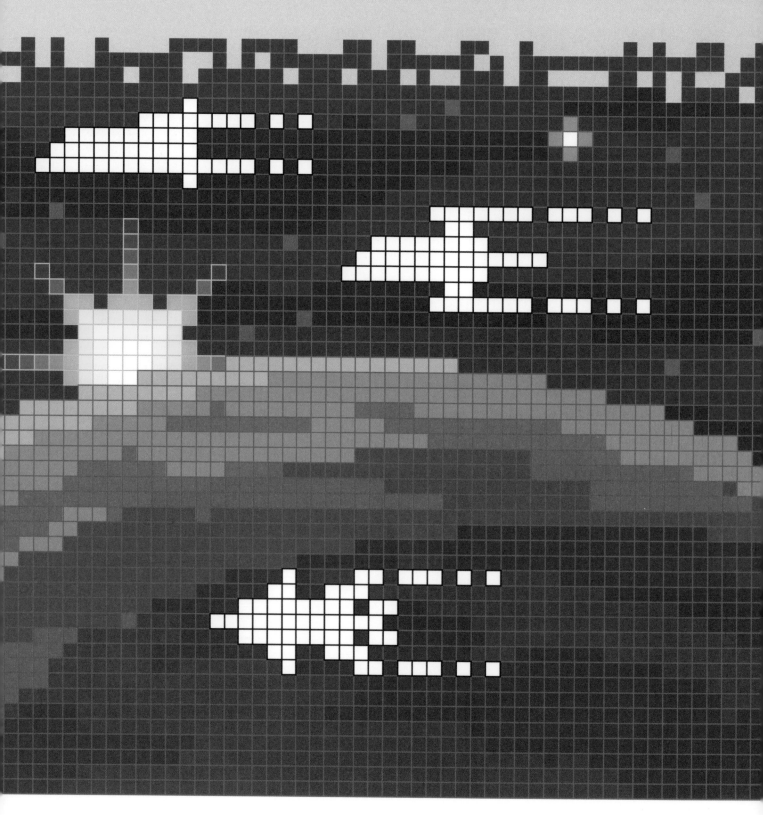

Uh-oh! Don't look now, but there seem to be some space dragons behind us. Hopefully they're not hungry!

Infantry Droid

Infantry droids are the Battle Fleet's shock troops. They can fight in any environment and they never give up. Zap! Zap! Whirr...Zap!

Vampoid

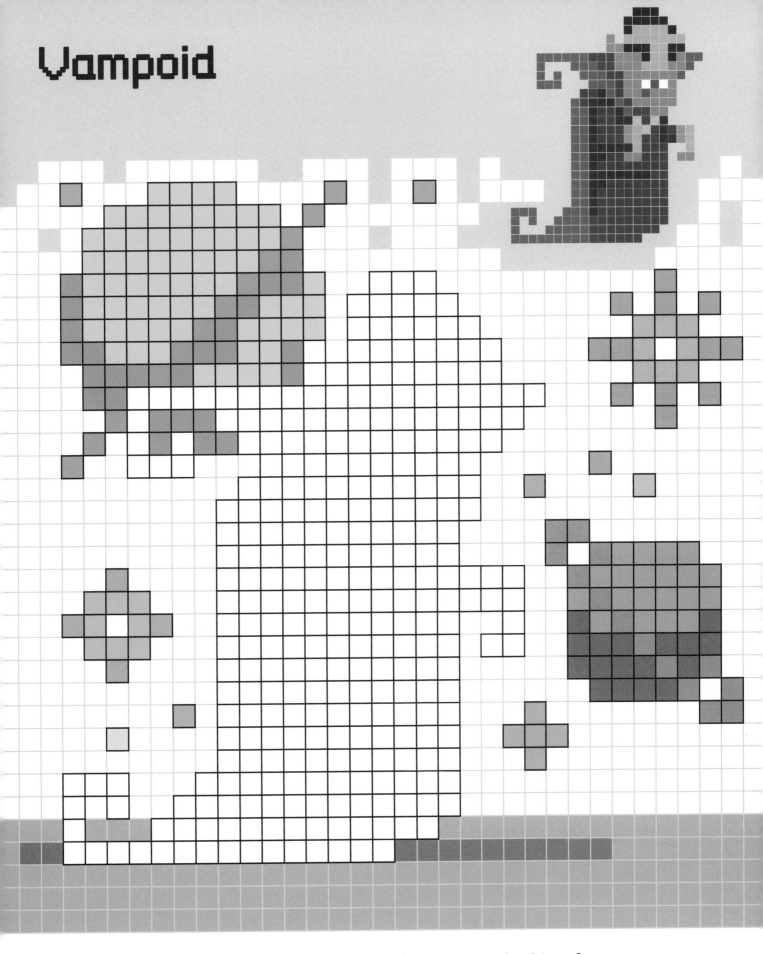

Vampoid stalks the dark edge of the solar system, looking for prey.

Shoot Out!

Lord Blob has been found, and infantry droids have been sent to take him captive. But his Blobbiness won't come without a fight! Ka-pow! Ka-pow!

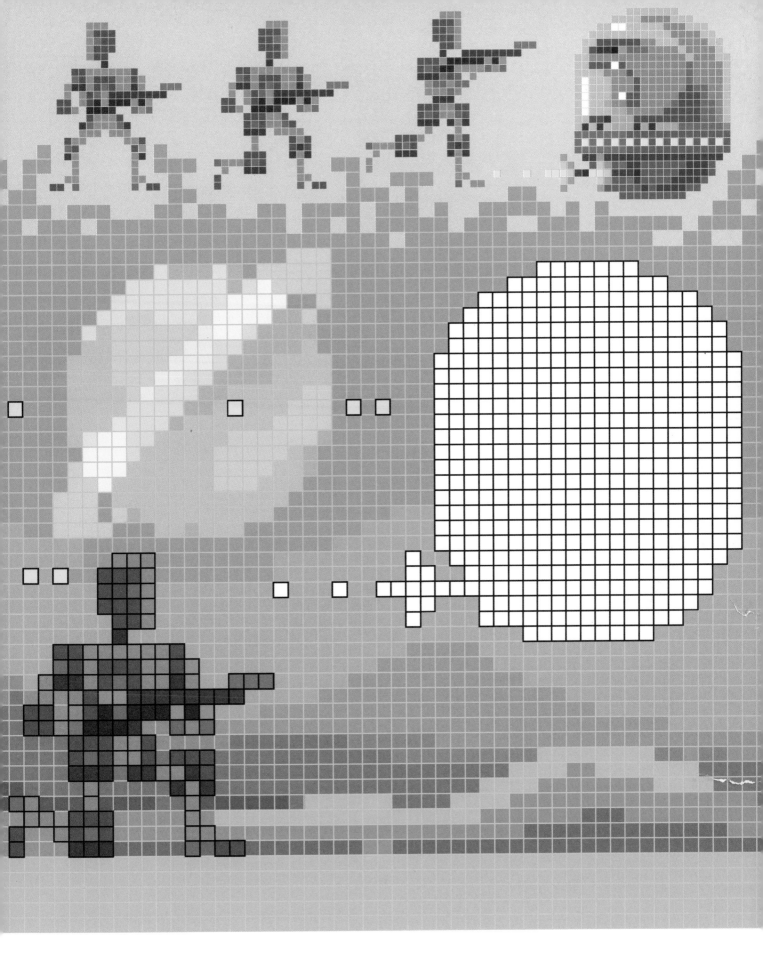

Fly Past

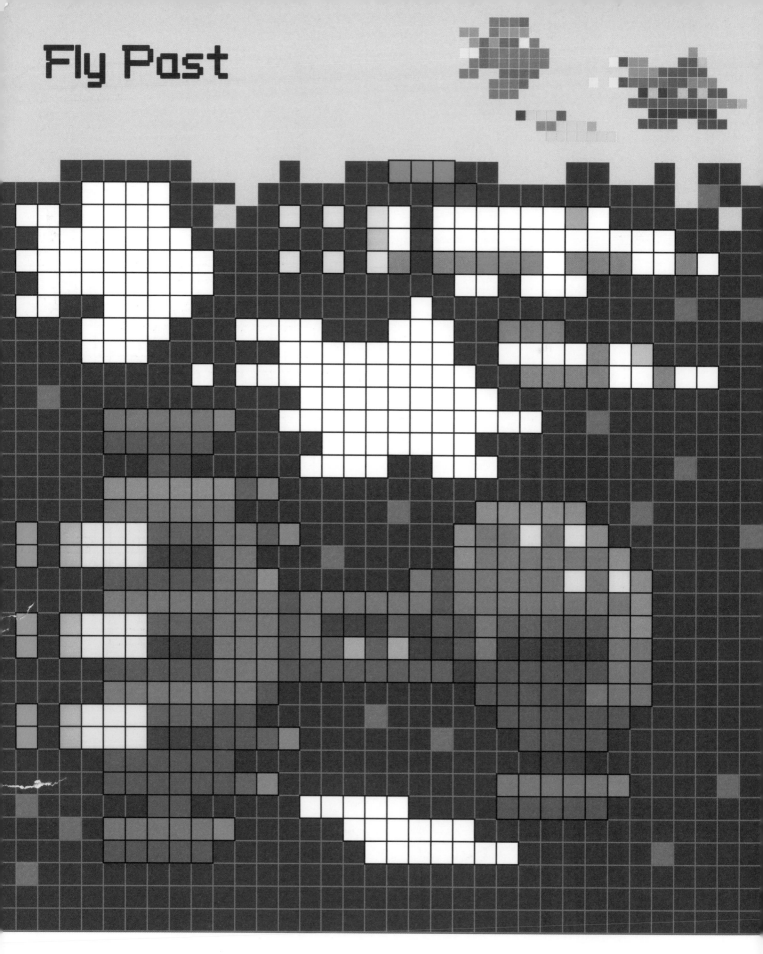

The galaxy is safe again! There's a triumphant fly past of Battle Fleet ships! Hip hip hooray!